Contents

Schofield

Welcome to this book

Glossary

SECTION 1

Tests 1 to 12, covering: 4

Spelling: Common letter strings with different pronunciations. Common homophones. Spelling rules and patterns: plurals (words ending with **f**); **ible**, **able**; high-frequency words with unstressed vowels.

Word structure: Adding **ive**, **ist**, **able**. Compound words. Hyphens. Exploring common roots.

Vocabulary: Using word structures and common roots to work out meaning. Synonyms and shades of meaning. Adverbs. Idioms.

Sentence structure: Exploring sentence types and alternative sentence constructions; adding phrases and clauses; using a range of connectives.

Punctuation: Commas to mark clauses and phrases; avoiding comma splice. Setting out and punctuating dialogue. Apostrophes for possession (including plurals). Identifying more advanced punctuation (dash, colon).

Grammar: Choosing words for impact and effect; figurative and expressive language. Language features of different text types. Verb tenses; using auxiliary verbs. Formal and informal language. Direct and reported speech.

Section 1 Writing task: Jam sandwich!   16

Section 1 Proofreading task: Ricky the runner   17

SECTION 2

Tests 1 to 12, covering all the above, plus: 18

Spelling: Different spellings of 'shun' endings. Regular spelling patterns (soft **g**, soft **c**) and rules relating to double consonants.

Word structure: Less common prefixes. Word families.

Vocabulary: Formal and informal synonyms. Words with multiple antonyms or with several meanings. Using prefixes to create antonyms. Onomatopoeia. Everyday metaphors.

Sentence structure: Question types. Combining sentences; pronouns as connectives. Adapting sentence structures to different story text types.

Punctuation: Punctuation in longer sentences. Using brackets and dashes.

Grammar: Similes; metaphors. Standard English. Noun types. Possessive pronouns.

Section 2 Writing task: The tortoise and the hare   30

Section 2 Proofreading task: Fruity fruit salad   31

SECTION 3

Tests 1 to 12, covering all the above, plus: 32

Spelling: Spelling unstressed vowels in polysyllabic words. Regular spelling patterns (**ie**, **ei**). Adding vowel suffixes. **i** before **e**.

Word structure: Less common prefixes (**pro**, **sus**, **ir**) and suffixes (**ify**, **ise**, **ism**, **ity**).

Vocabulary: Words with an everyday and a subject-specific meaning; technical words. Word formation; compound words.

Sentence structure: Adapting sentence construction to different text types, purposes or readers. Prepositional phrases. Combining clauses.

Punctuation: Use and misuse of apostrophes and commas. Punctuation to clarify meaning; commas to embed.

Grammar: Words for specific aims. Text types. Prepositions. Modal verbs.

Section 3 Writing task: Outraged   44

Section 3 Proofreading task: The genie of the bedside lamp   45

Progress chart   46

Section 1   Test 1

A   WARM-UP

Add an adverb.

1 She spoke _____ about her feelings.

2 He was _____ punished for the crime.

3 _____ , they walked off down the road.

Add one or two consonants to complete the words.

4 w o r __   w o r __   w o r __

5 w o r __ __   w o r __ __   w o r __ __

Put the letters in order to make a word.

6 e g s s u   _____

7 a c h t w   _____

8 e h l o w   _____

Add the same prefix to each set of words.

9 ____most   ____though   ____mighty

10 ____change   ____claim   ____tend

B   WORD WORK

Write the root word. Underline the prefixes and suffix/es.

1 d i s a p p r o v i n g l y   _____

2 i m p e r s o n a l   _____

Change the noun in **bold** into a plural.

3 one **thief**   →   three _____

4 one **Princess**   →   _____

5 Penny's **puppy**   →   _____

6 the brave **child**   →   _____

Sort the words into two groups.

frustrated livid irritated enraged

7 **very angry:**   _____

8 **quite angry:**   _____

Add two synonyms to each group.

9 **very happy:**   _____

10 **quite happy:**   _____

C   SENTENCE WORK

Complete the sentence.

1 After _____ , we had a great time.

2 Despite _____ , we had a great time.

3 Although _____ , we had a great time.

4 Before _____ , we had a great time.

Improve the sentence by adding three suitable words.

5 The _____ _____ man walked along the road, singing _____ to himself.

6 Ellie gazed _____ out of the window at the _____ city _____ .

7 The _____ dog looked at him with his _____ _____ eyes.

8 The women looked _____ around the _____ _____ room.

It was beginning to rain, big heavy drops fell from the sky, the picnic was over

9 What is wrong with the punctuation? _____

10 Write it correctly.

X There is only one correct answer.   X There is more than one correct answer.

Schofield&Sims

English Skills **4**

writing sentences

spelling proofreading

comma

vocabulary

letters

noun

conjunctions

words

correct

grammar

describe

past tense

spelling

rhyme

phrase

tasks

answer

suffix

adjectives

prefix

verbs

capital letters

vowel

writing

ideas

develop

proofreading

understanding
& choosing
words

skills

writing *punctuation*

end of a story

Name

The **English Skills** tests give you plenty of practice in using your literacy skills. With regular practice, your skills will quickly improve. Each **English Skills** book is divided into three sections. When you finish a section, complete one column of the **Progress chart** on page 46. Full instructions are given.

The **Glossary** below may help you to tackle the tests. It gives examples that may help you to understand a question. You can also use a **dictionary** to check the spelling or find the meaning of a word, but remember that some words have more than one meaning. A **thesaurus** will help you to find words with similar meanings (synonyms). Some thesauruses also list opposites (antonyms).

Glossary

acrostic	a poem in which the first letter of each line spells out the poem's subject
brackets	look like this **( )** and are used to add extra information to a sentence
clause	a part of a sentence. It includes a verb.
compound sentence	a sentence where two equal clauses are joined with **and**, **but** or **so** (e.g., **It was late and he was tired.**)
direct speech	a written version of the exact words spoken, which appear in speech marks (e.g., **"I am very tired," said Annie.**)
embed	to add extra information to the middle of a sentence (e.g., in the sentence **Daniel James, aged 10, was the winner**, the **aged 10** has been embedded)
formal language	the language and sentence structure that we use in special 'formal' situations
idiom	an expression that is not meant to be taken literally (e.g., the idiom **a piece of cake** refers to a task that is easy to complete; it has nothing to do with cake)
imperative	a command or order (e.g., **Give that to me.**)
informal language	the everyday language and sentence structure that we use with people we know. When written down, informal language is similar to spoken language.
metaphor	a comparison that does **not** use **like** or **as** (e.g., **The moon was a silver coin.**)
noun phrase	a group of words built around the noun or naming word (e.g., **the new library**)
onomatopoeia	a word that sounds like the noise it describes (e.g., **pop, sizzle**)
preposition	a word that is usually followed by a noun phrase. Many prepositions tell you about time, position or direction (e.g., **at**, **under**, **between**, **over**).
pronoun	a word used in place of a noun (e.g., **he**, **his**, **theirs**)
proper noun	the name of a person, place or organisation (e.g., **Dr Naidoo**, **Wales**, the **BBC**)
pun	a humorous play on words. You use on purpose words that sound the same but have different meanings (e.g., **Where do polar bears vote? The North Poll!**).
reported speech	a written version of words spoken, in which you report what was said without using the actual words (e.g., **Annie said she was very tired.**)
rhetorical question	a question that is used for effect rather than to be answered (e.g., **Why me?**)
simile	a descriptive comparison in which a writer compares one thing to another using the words **like** or **as** (e.g., **The moon was like a silver coin.**)
Standard English	the accepted rules and patterns of written English (e.g., you might say **There was this man** but in Standard English you would write **There was a man**)
syllable	a small part of a longer word. Each syllable makes a separate sound or beat when you say the word (e.g., **fol** / **low** / **ing** has three syllables).

Section 1 Test 2

A WARM-UP

Complete the simile using a suitable animal.

1 mad as _____

2 cheerful as _____

3 lazy as _____

4 greedy as _____

Add the missing suffix to complete the word.

5 w i l l _____ n e s s

6 w o r t h _____ n e s s

7 f o o l _____ n e s s

Write a word using these letters.
The letters must be used in this order.

8 t g t   _____

9 p s b   _____

10 c m n   _____

B WORD WORK

One consonant or two? Write in the missing letters.

1 s h a ____ o w (d)

2 s h a ____ o w (l)

Underline the correct word of the two that appear in brackets.

3 The water (sloped / slopped) around.

4 How did you know? _____
_____

5 Edgar (stares / stairs) out of the window.

6 How did you know? _____
_____

7 Write the homophone.

   morning _____   **seen** _____

All three words come from the same root.
Underline the root.

8 thermal thermometer thermostat

9 aquarium aqueduct Aquarius

What do the root words mean?

10 _____ = _____   _____ = _____

C SENTENCE WORK

Turn each sentence into a question (Q) and an imperative (I).

1 Let's go to the cinema.   Q: _____
                               I: _____

2 You could bake a cake.   Q: _____
                               I: _____

3 We could form two teams.   Q: _____
                               I: _____

Add words to create the given mood.

4 **calm, peaceful**   The _____ moonlight gave a _____ glow to the _____ trees.

5 **threatening, sinister** The _____ moonlight gave a _____ glow to the _____ trees.

6 Underline the word that best describes your additions.   verbs adjectives nouns adverbs

Rewrite the phrase using three words only.

7 the instruments belonging to the band   _____

8 the party held for the three brothers   _____

9 the club belonging to the supporters   _____

10 the staffroom for the teachers   _____

X There is only one correct answer.   X There is more than one correct answer.   5

Section 1 Test 3

A WARM-UP

lion sandwich

1 Write a sentence using these words.

_____

2 Write a question using these words.

_____

Add the missing vowels.
You may use a letter twice if necessary.

a e u

3 b _ _ _ t y   **5** b _ c _ _ s e

4 _ _ t _ m n   **6** p _ _ se

7 These words and prefixes are mixed up.
Write them correctly.

minisecond microbus nanochip

_____

8 What do the word roots have in common?

_____

Write two more words with the root shown in **bold**.

9 mini   _____

10 micro   _____

B WORD WORK

Write in the missing word.

I can do it myself.

1 She can do it _____ .

2 We can do it _____ .

3 They can do it _____ .

Make three words.

press im de ing ly ure

4 _____   **6** _____

5 _____

Write the meaning of the phrase.

7 to turn over a new leaf

_____

8 to feel under the weather

_____

9 That rings a bell!

_____

10 What do you notice about these phrases?

_____

_____

C SENTENCE WORK

Continue the sentence, to explain or tell the reader more.

1 People are uneasy _____

2 Josh ran through the door _____

3 Fold the paper in half _____

4 The dog watched the cat _____

Mobile phones should be switched off.

Rewrite the sentence as

5 a question: _____

6 an imperative: _____

7 an exclamation: _____

Write the dialogue correctly.

8 We must leave said David.   _____

9 When asked Anna.   _____

10 Very soon David replied.   _____

X There is only one correct answer.   X There is more than one correct answer.

Section 1 Test 4

A WARM-UP

Add the correct word endings.

1 The rain fell heavy_____, make_____ the
fields mist_____ and grey.

2 Luck_____, the drive_____ stop_____ the car
before hit_____ the two parked lorry_____ .

Complete the word sum.

3 **occupy + ing** = _____

4 **occupy + ed** = _____

5 **occupy + er** = _____

6 Write the homophone.

threw _____   **heard** _____

Complete the alliterative pattern.

ten tigers tickling to tease

7 nine newts _____

8 seven swans _____

9 five frogs _____

10 two turtles _____

B WORD WORK

The same letter string is missing from all these words.
Write it in.

1 e n _____   a l t h _____

2 t h r _____   t h _____ t

3 What do you notice? _____
_____

4 Write two more words with this letter string.
_____

Draw a line to join the word to another word
with the same root.

5 **noun**   anniversary

6 **voice**   announce

7 **annual**   vocal

Write two words that use the root word.

8 **graph** _____

9 **circum** _____

10 Underline the synonyms of **sadly**.

politely dejectedly gleefully dismally

C SENTENCE WORK

Complete the simile.

1 A still pond is like _____

2 Autumn leaves are like _____

3 A volcano is like _____

4 A poppy is like _____

Cross out some of the words and write new ones that make the performance sound more impressive.

5 Cleaver sent a good high ball into the penalty area and Jones got it into the net.
_____

6 The goalkeeper jumped well and knocked the ball just over the crossbar.
_____

7 After some good play from Cleaver, Robinson sent a good ball past the stranded keeper.
_____

Add the missing commas.

8 Although it was dark I knew someone was following me.

9 Before we begin let's check everyone is here.

10 The two children who were very tired soon fell fast asleep.

Section 1 Test 5

A WARM-UP

Complete the sentence.

1 Sam made tea. Meanwhile, _____

_____

2 Sam made tea. Suddenly, _____

_____

3 Sam made tea. Afterwards, _____

_____

Add the same three-letter word to all three words.

4 ____t h   s____c h   h____d

5 c r____u r e   g r____e s t   s w____

6 f l a v____   c o l____   j____n e y

7 Underline the word that is **not** a real word.

artist novelist photographist stockist

Write three more words ending with **ist**.

8 _____

9 _____

10 _____

B WORD WORK

Add **ible** or **able**.

1 suit_____   enjoy_____   fashion_____

2 terr_____   ed_____   horr_____

3 How are the **able** words different from the **ible** words?

_____

_____

Add a word after the hyphen to complete the compound word.

4 break-____   *Clue: burglary*

5 passer-____   *Clue: someone walking past*

6 Add a prefix before the hyphen.

____-operate   ____-stick   ____-president

7 Write three more examples of words with hyphens.

_____

Write a definition.

8 **disapprovingly:** _____

9 **enthusiastically:** _____

10 **courteously:** _____

C SENTENCE WORK

Rewrite the sentence with the word or phrase in **bold** at the beginning.

1 The tent collapsed **as I stood up.** _____

2 The room was **strangely** silent. _____

3 There was a faint rumble **from far away.** _____

Write **formal** or **informal** beside each sentence to identify the type of language used.

4 I was travelling along Northgate Road when the accident occurred. _____

5 There I was minding my own business and guess what happened? _____

Give one reason for each of your answers.

6 _____

7 _____

What punctuation mark is hidden by the symbol?

8 He might have won a thousand pounds ▲ or even a million ♠

▲ is _____   ♠ is _____

9 For this experiment you will need the following▼ a bottle● filter paper and a paper clip.

▼ is _____   ● is _____

10 Sally♦sadly♦▼ Are you sure■   *Clue: this is a line of dialogue from a playscript*

♦ is _____   ▼ is _____   ■ is _____

X There is only one correct answer.   X There is more than one correct answer.

A   WARM-UP

Write three sentences using these words only.

waited they nervously

1 _____

2 _____

3 _____

4 Add the **ing** ending.

spiral_____   crackle _____   explode _____

Draw a line to join the word to a suffix and make a new word.

5 **free**   ship

6 **false**   hood

7 **partner**   dom

Write the noun as a plural.

8 **battery**   _____

9 **box**   _____

10 **knife**   _____

B   WORD WORK

Add the missing vowels.

1 g __ r d __ n

2 g __ l d __ n

3 h __ __ v __ n

4 d __ f f __ r __ n t

5 Add the suffix **tion**.

inform_____   tempt_____   expect_____

6 What do you notice?

_____

_____

7 Underline the two synonyms that sound the most formal.

lots ample heaps loads bags sufficient

Write two more formal synonyms.

8 **get**   _____

9 **give**   _____

10 **tell**   _____

C   SENTENCE WORK

1 Write eight verbs that would be suitable to fill the gap.

Mr Jackson _____ come home.

_____

2 Write two words that would form the past tense.   _____

3 Write two words that would form the future tense.   _____

Write two adverbs that give different views of the character.

4 "What are you doing?" asked the boy _____ / _____.

5 "Come on then," said Maria _____ / _____ .

6 "I'll take that," the woman said _____ / _____ .

Continue the sentence.

7 The year is divided into four seasons: _____

8 Jack finally arrived – _____

9 Before he knew it, _____

10 We had pizza for tea (_____

Section 1 Test 7

A WARM-UP

Write the imperative as a question.

1 Stand up.

_____

2 Come here.

_____

3 Go and play.

_____

Add the same prefix to all three words.

4 _____code   _____form   _____flate

5 _____place   _____move   _____view

6 _____take   _____count   _____lead

Write in the missing word.

it's its

7 _____ great here!

8 The dog buried _____ bone.

9 The tree shook _____ leaves.

10 I hope _____ not too late.

B WORD WORK

Change the nouns into plurals.

1 piano____   radio____

2 potato____   hero____

3 What is the same about the spelling of
the singular words?

_____

4 How are the plurals different?

_____

_____

These words are mixed up. Write them correctly.

sublight atmomerge micronatural supersphere

5 _____   7 _____

6 _____   8 _____

Write three words that use the root word.

9 **verb** (meaning **word**):

_____

10 **uni** (meaning **one**):

_____

C SENTENCE WORK

Write three sentences that contain these words.

thieves boxes

1 **a simple sentence:** _____

2 **a compound sentence:** _____

3 **a sentence with a connective:** _____

Complete the phrase and add apostrophes to show which of these groups owns what.

the driver the bakers the crew the horses

4 _____ oven   6 _____ stables

5 _____ van   7 _____ spaceship

Complete the sentence, choosing words for effect.

8 The man _____ into the woods, branches _____ under his feet, the beast _____ at his coat.

9 He saw its _____ eyes, round like _____ . He smelt its _____ coat of _____ fur.

10 What type of story are both these sentences from? Underline your chosen answer.

science fiction horror story school story

Section 1 Test 8

A WARM-UP

Add an adverb to make the statement stronger.

1 This is _____ wrong.

2 _____ , no-one can agree with this!

One consonant or two? Write in the missing letters.

3 m o ___ e n t (**m**)

4 c o ___ e e (**f**)

5 t a ___ o o (**t**)

Add the missing vowels. *Clue: all foods*

6 b _ n _ n _   s _ m _ s _

7 r a v _ _ l _   r _ s _ t t _

The flob is an imaginary creature.
Complete these similes to describe it.

8 It moves like _____

9 It sounds like _____

10 It eats like _____

B WORD WORK

Add the missing letters.

1 p o s s _ b l e   **3** r e m a r k _ b l e

2 v i s _ b l e   **4** r e a s o n _ b l e

Add a prefix and/or a suffix to make a new word.

5 ____ take ____   *Clue: wrong*

6 ____ prison ____   *Clue: locked up*

7 active ____   *Clue: a task to do*

Complete the well-known saying and write
a definition.

8 you can't judge a book by _____

　　　means: _____

　　　_____

9 got out of bed on _____

　　　means: _____

10 over the _____

　　　means: _____

C SENTENCE WORK

Write a sentence to follow the headline.

1 Class G takes the plunge! _____

_____

2 School concert raises the roof! _____

_____

3 Bookbusters are go! _____

_____

Write the tense used for each line of this script.

4 **Ben and Angie enter, running.** _____

5 **Ben: No-one saw us.** _____

6 **Angie: What shall we do if someone comes?** _____

Rewrite the sentence as direct speech.

7 Eve asked Ross if he was OK. _____

8 Mr Bahra said his house was ruined. _____

9 The genie told him the magic word [yoyo]. _____

10 Lucy asked for her size [size 2]. _____

X There is only one correct answer.   X There is more than one correct answer.   **11**

Section 1　Test 9

A　WARM-UP

Continue the sentence.

1　Terry was anxious in case _____

_____

2　Terry was anxious despite _____

_____

3　Terry was anxious whenever _____

_____

4　Terry was anxious until _____

_____

Write two words with this root.

5　**tri** (means 3) _____

6　**octo** (means 8) _____

7　**dec** (means 10) _____

Cross out the word that is wrongly spelt.
Write the correct spelling.

8　special social parcial _____

9　yoyos echos solos _____

10　reliable edable adorable _____

B　WORD WORK

Add the missing syllable.

1　f r i g h t ____ i n g

2　f o r ____ l y

3　i n ____ e s t

4　g e n ____ a l

5　Write the new word that is made by adding the suffix **tion**.

protect _____

invent _____

perfect _____

illustrate _____

6　What do you notice?

_____

_____

Write three words using the root word.

7　**child** _____

8　**pain** _____

9　**hand** _____

10　**move** _____

C　SENTENCE WORK

What type of instructional text is each instruction taken from?

1　**Bake until the top is golden and the fruit soft.**　from _____

2　**Select the text you want to change.**　from _____

3　**Cut carefully along the dotted lines.**　from _____

Complete the sentence about instructions.

4　In instructions, verbs are usually _____

5　Adverbs are used to _____

6　Adjectives are used to _____

Rewrite the sentence so that the words and/or phrases are in a different order.

7　The door opened easily much to his surprise. _____

8　Jack ran out of the door, grabbing the golden egg.

_____

9　Faintly, a light shone from far away. _____

10　Amy forgot her worries for a while huddled by the fire.

_____

X There is only one correct answer.　X There is more than one correct answer.

A   WARM-UP

Complete the sentence.

1 Gradually, _____

2 Surprisingly, _____

3 Determinedly, _____

4 Write in the colours needed to complete these sayings.

to see _____   to feel _____

a _____ area   a _____ opportunity

5 Write six compound words using the word **work**.

_____

_____

Add the missing vowels.

Clue: all musical instruments

6 b _ n j _

7 c _ l l _

8 p _ c c _ l _

9 b _ n g _

10 p _ _ n _

B   WORD WORK

Add the missing letters.

1 s e v _ r a l   2 b u s _ n e s s

Cross out the words that are wrongly spelt.
Write the correct spelling.

3 I had sereal for brekfast.

_____

4 I don't like marmelade. _____

5 Lunch was too chickin samwichis and an appul.

_____

6 Write four words using these roots only.

auto para graph chute photo

_____

_____

Use the same roots to make two words that do **not** exist.

7 _____   8 _____

Write the meaning of the root word.

9 **auto** = _____   10 **photo** = _____

C   SENTENCE WORK

Write three different sentences using the word **shape**.

1 **an instruction:** _____

2 **a headline:** _____

3 **a descriptive sentence:** _____

Write these formal statements so that they sound informal.

4 I am completely blameless. _____

5 Unfortunately, I am not able to provide that information. _____

Write this informal sentence so that it sounds formal.

6 People shouldn't do things like that. _____

Use brackets to add an extra comment or piece of information.

7 Auntie Agnes is coming on Saturday (_____

8 My name is Richard (_____

9 **Pirate 1** (_____ : Man overboard!

10 Raj (_____ came to tea.

X There is only one correct answer.   X There is more than one correct answer.

Section 1   Test 11

A   WARM-UP

Use the word **kitten** in each of the following.

1 a sentence: _____

_____

2 a headline: _____

_____

3 a question: _____

_____

4 an order: _____

_____

Write three verbs to use in place of

5 likes: _____

6 dislikes: _____

Add the missing vowels.

Clue: all animals

7 p _ m _

8 _ r m _ d _ l l _

9 d _ n g _

10 k _ _ l _

B   WORD WORK

Underline the correct spelling.

1 slipery slippery slipperey slipprey

2 normaly normaley normally normerly

Add the suffix **able**.

3 rely _____   envy _____

4 value _____   adore _____

What two spelling rules did you use?

5 _____

6 _____

Auto means **self** or **one's own**.
Use this information to define

7 automatic: _____

8 autograph: _____

Trans means **across**.
Use this information to define

9 transatlantic: _____

10 transplant: _____

_____

C   SENTENCE WORK

Is this a simile or a metaphor? Write your answer.

1 Clouds are like cotton wool. _____

2 Cotton wool clouds float by. _____

3 Clouds are cotton wool in the sky. _____

4 Clouds are white and soft as cotton wool. _____

Write a simile and a metaphor about snowflakes.

5 simile: _____

6 metaphor: _____

7 Add the punctuation to the dialogue.

Zoe Have you seen this film

Jack No I havent

8 Write the dialogue as direct speech.

_____

_____

9 Write the dialogue as reported speech. _____

10 Write a sentence using the words **girl rabbit although**.

_____

14   X There is only one correct answer.   X There is more than one correct answer.

A WARM-UP

Write a simile to describe

1 grass: _____

2 a spider's web: _____

3 lightning: _____

4 Underline the word that you **cannot** add **able** to.

drink port bend water work

Add a prefix and a suffix.

5 ____place_____ *Clue: substitute*

6 ____sign____ *Clue: someone who designs*

7 ____part____ *Clue: leaving*

Add a letter to the middle of the word to make another word. Write the new word.

8 though _____

9 crate _____

10 widow _____

B WORD WORK

Add the suffix **tion**.

1 combine _____

2 vary _____

What two spelling rules did you use?

3 _____

4 _____

Imagine that the word in **bold** really existed. What would it mean?

5 bivision: _____

6 supership: _____

Write a definition of these compound words, found in a computer manual.

7 desktop: _____
_____

8 download: _____
_____

9 online: _____
_____

10 shortcut: _____
_____

C SENTENCE WORK

Rewrite these statements in Standard English.

1 It felt real exciting seeing in the paper the picture what I drew.

_____

2 I seen her eating them cakes what you brought.

_____

3 They was there. I seen them with me own eyes. _____

4 I didn't say nothing to no-one. _____

5 Write a metaphor to describe a sunset. _____

Put a tick if the punctuation is correct. Put a cross if it is not.

6 "Dont drink that" screamed Josie. "Its Jakes magic potion." ____

7 He stood still. He listened. Not a sound could be heard. ____

8 The room was empty, there was no carpet on the floor. ____

Write the incorrect items correctly.

9 _____

10 _____

Section 1 Writing task: Jam sandwich!

Task

A lorry carrying jam crashes in the town centre. Write a newspaper article or report based on this incident. The headline is **Jam sandwich!**

Hints

Before you start:

- Think what the article might be about.
- Consider what your reader will want to know.
- Work out what happened, where, when and why, and who was involved.
- Consider whether there are other vital details that should be included.
- Decide how to organise and set out your article.

As you write:

- Think how a reporter would write the article.
- Choose your words carefully.
- Try out sentences to see if they sound like those in a real newspaper report.

Continue on a separate sheet.

Check

- When you have finished, check through your article.
- Edit and proofread it.
- Make sure that everything looks and sounds right.

Section 1 Proofreading task: Ricky the runner

Task

Proofread this character description from a story.

Hints

- Check that everything is clear and sounds right.
- Check the punctuation and capital letters.
- Check the spelling.
- Change anything that does not look or sound right.

Let me tell you about my bruther Ricky. Hes ate years old has spikey hair like a spidder plant and a crookid smile that some peepel think is qute me I just find it anoying.

Normerly you will find him lieing on his bed with the ramote in one hand and a samwidge (useualy sosage in the other TVs the most importunt thing in his life. and the ownley way to get his attenshun is to swich it of.

Now belive it or not he says hes turnd over a knew leaf and want to be a sporting supperstar just like that I'm going to be in the Olympics he says. its quiet possable Ill be a gold medalest he tells us the boys mad

Enyway now hes joging rownd the howse making us all sufer if that werent bad enuff, we have to put up with all his horribul sports kit evereywhere. am I being unreesonabul

Extra

On a separate sheet of paper, write a brief description of an imaginary brother or sister who dreams of becoming a television star.

A WARM-UP

Write three sentences and a question using these words only.

ready finally was she

1 _____

2 _____

3 _____

4 _____

Write two words using these letters.
The letters must be used in this order.

5 **m p t** _____

6 **j m t** _____

7 **a t n** _____

Underline the suffix that you **cannot** add to the word in **bold**.

8 **origin** al ate able s

9 **act** ive or ist tion

10 **forgive** able ness ing tion

B WORD WORK

1 The same four-letter string is missing from all these words. Write it in.

s h ____ e r s   b ____ e r   w ____   c ____

2 What do you notice?

_____

Add a prefix and/or a suffix to make a new word.

3 script_____ *Clue: holy writings*

4 _____script_____ *Clue: for medicine*

5 _____script_____ *Clue: PS*

6 _____script_____ *Clue: on a gravestone*

7 The root word **script** means _____.

Write a definition of the word or words in **bold**.

8 **Score** along the dotted lines.

score: _____

9 He listened to **heavy metal**.

heavy metal: _____

10 I searched the **web**.

web: _____

C SENTENCE WORK

Complete this sentence to make Joe sound

1 **happy:** "Listen to this," _____ Joe, _____

2 **shocked:** "Listen to this," _____ Joe, _____

3 **worried:** "Listen to this," _____ Joe, _____

Cross out the nouns and replace them with proper names.

4 That player plays for that team. _____

5 I saw a woman going into a shop. _____

6 This man is in charge of this organisation. _____

Why has the writer used brackets?

7 Fold the corners into the centre (see Diagram 2). _____

8 Nelson (1758–1805) was a famous sea admiral. _____

9 Foxes live in many urban (built-up) areas. _____

10 Sally (whom I never did trust) went straight to the teacher. _____

X There is only one correct answer.   X There is more than one correct answer.

Section 2 Test 2

A WARM-UP

Rewrite the sentence, first as an imperative (I) and then as a question (Q).

The pizza is in the oven.

1 I: _____

2 Q: _____

Make three words.

fit un ful ing ly

3 _____   **5** _____

4 _____

Write three words that end with the suffix.

6 _____ment _____ment _____ment

7 _____ic _____ic _____ic

Put the letters in order to make a word.

8 d n o s u   _____

9 e g h i w   _____

10 e g h n o u   _____

B WORD WORK

Add the missing vowels.

1 e x c _ l l _ n t

2 s e v _ r _ l

3 d e f _ n _ t e

Read the words aloud. Underline the odd one out.

4 too two to tow

5 so sow saw sew

6 Why are the odd ones out different?

_____

7 What do you notice about the other words in each group?

_____

_____

_____

8 Underline the root word.

perilously triumphantly

Write a definition.

9 perilously: _____

10 triumphantly: _____

C SENTENCE WORK

Continue the sentence using one of these words.

who where which

1 Once there was a poor farmer _____

2 There was once a faraway kingdom _____

3 They huddled round the fire, _____

4 George was a stonecutter _____

Some words have been crossed out. Write new words that sound more formal.

5 They ~~got rid of~~ _____ the ~~stuff~~ _____.

6 They ~~got hold of~~ _____ the ~~gear~~ _____.

7 He seemed ~~a bit shady~~ _____.

Underline the correct word of the three that appear in brackets.

8 There were once three (sisters / sister's / sisters').

9 The three (brothers / brother's / brothers') home was tiny.

10 (Helens / Helen's / Helens') donkey trotted off down the road.

Section 2 Test 3

A WARM-UP

Complete the sentence.

1 Dan did not speak although _____

_____

2 Dan did not speak until _____

_____

3 Dan did not speak in case _____

_____

Add one letter to make a new word.

4 hear _____

5 word _____

6 wait _____

7 favour _____

Add the same short word to complete all three longer words.

8 a v e r ____   i m ____   v i l l ____

9 h a r b ____   h ____   f l ____

10 Change the words into plurals.

factory _____   **marsh** _____

industry _____   **valley** _____

B WORD WORK

1 Add **full** or **ful**.

____er   ____y   doubt____   faith____

2 What spelling pattern do you notice?

_____

3 Add **all** or **al**.

____ways   ____most   ____ready   over____

4 What spelling pattern do you notice?

_____

Add prefixes and/or suffixes to make three new words.

5 lone _____

6 cover _____

7 real _____

Add the missing word to the well-known phrase.

8 as fit as _____

9 as cool as _____

10 as blind as _____

C SENTENCE WORK

What a mess! You wouldn't believe it. Norma's cottage? More like Nor–mess cottage!

1 Underline the two words that best describe the style of this story.

chatty formal warm jokey descriptive

Give three reasons to explain your choice.

2 _____

3 _____

4 _____

Complete these metaphors.

5 The river _____

6 His eyes _____

7 Fog _____

Cross out any unnecessary commas.

8 One night, as he lay asleep, under the stars, Angelo had, a dream.

9 For several minutes, the wizard looked, at him, in silence.

10 The old woman, hurriedly, hid the food, in the woodpile, hoping no-one, would look there.

X There is only one correct answer.   X There is more than one correct answer.

Section 2 Test 4

A WARM-UP

Write a sentence using one of these words.

entirely relatively importantly

1 _____

2 _____

3 _____

4 Make six words using these letters only.

   o n t w

   _____

Remove one letter to make a new word.

5 **beard**   _____

6 **monkey**   _____

7 **through**   _____

Underline the correct spelling.

8 flexable flexeble flexible

9 reversable reverseble reversible

10 forgivable forgiveble forgivible

B WORD WORK

Underline the word that is **not** a real word.

1 autograph automobile autonature

2 microscope microbitus microphone

3 telecut telephone telescope

Write two homophones.

4 **road**   _____

5 **you**   _____

6 **by**   _____

7 **rain**   _____

Sort the words into two groups.

city collar cope cell case cub cycle cyst

8 **soft c:**   _____

9 **hard c:**   _____

10 What letters usually follow a soft **c**?

   _____

C SENTENCE WORK

Continue the sentence.

1 He stopped suddenly as if _____

2 Suddenly darkness descended as though _____

3 He would continue his search as long as _____

4 Amanda was the oldest sister as well as _____

Sort the words into two groups that could be used to describe a character.

uncaring generous bold snivelling devious feeble dependable cheerful

5 **appealing:**   _____

6 **unappealing:**   _____

Underline the correct word of those that appear in brackets.

7 It was (their / there / they're) day off.

8 I believe (their / there / they're) away on holiday.

9 I hope (your / you're) coming.

10 I shall put this in (your / you're) folder.

| X | There is only one correct answer. | X | There is more than one correct answer. |

A **WARM-UP**

Rewrite the sentence in a more formal way.

1 I ditched the rest.

_____

2 The film was slated.

_____

3 The kids soon perked up.

_____

Change one letter to make a homophone.
Write the new word and its meaning.

4 **peek** (a look)   _____

5 **steel** (a metal)   _____

6 **sun** (a star)   _____

Add different endings to complete the three words.

7 pack____   pack____   pack____

8 press____   press____   press____

9 assist____   assist____   assist____

10 stick____   stick____   stick____

B **WORD WORK**

1 What do the words have in common?

glug buzz slosh pop

_____

2 Add **ed** endings.

_____

3 Write four more words of the type you identified in question 1.

_____

Complete the word sum.

4 **collect** + **tion** = _____

5 **expand** + **sion** = _____

6 **decide** + **sion** = _____

7 What do you notice?

The **sion** words _____

8 Write four more words ending with **tion**.

_____

Underline the antonym of the word in **bold**.

9 **prosperous**   wealthy poor affluent

10 **trustworthy**   dishonest reliable solid

C **SENTENCE WORK**

Rewrite the sentence, rearranging the words, phrases and clauses and using the correct punctuation.

1 Everyone celebrated except Prince James when Princess Agnes was born.

_____

2 Many years ago there lived a dragon named Jem in a kingdom by the sea.

_____

3 The doors flew open suddenly just as everyone was sitting down to eat.

_____

Cross out the words that are wrong. Write them in correct Standard English.

4 I seen him pick up the book what was lying on the floor.   _____

5 I planted them bulbs and done some weeding.   _____

6 They was not afraid although they did not have no shelter.   _____

7 The man must of took the money what was on the table.   _____

Add nouns to fit the type of story.

8 **legend:** _____ faced the _____ .

9 **horror story:** _____ faced the _____ .

10 **school story:** _____ faced _____ .

X There is only one correct answer.   X There is more than one correct answer.

Section 2 Test 6

A   WARM-UP

Continue the sentence.

1   She spoke as if _____

_____

2   He crouched down as though _____

_____

3   They would remain there as long as _____

_____

These root words are mixed up. Write them correctly.

megaman   supercab   miniphone

4   _____   6   _____

5   _____

7   Write three words using the root word **super**.

_____

Add the missing letters.

Clue: use the name of a different family member to complete each word

8   h _ _ _ _ e d   10   s _ _ _ _ _ _ _

9   l e s _ _ _

B   WORD WORK

1   Add **ing** to these onomatopoeic words.

chug_____   hum _____   beep_____   snap_____

Write three onomatopoeic words that might describe the sounds made by

2   **an old car:**   _____

3   **water:**   _____

4   **animals:**   _____

5   Add the correct prefix.

il im in ir

___human   ___rational

___logical   ___polite

6   How do the prefixes change the word?

_____

_____

Write another word beginning with the prefix.

7   in_____

8   ir_____

9   il_____

10   im_____

C   SENTENCE WORK

Join the two sentences without using **and**.

1   Joe reached the top. He shouted down.   _____

2   He looked at the box. He wondered what was inside.

_____

3   The little goat trotted down the road. He munched a few leaves as he went.

_____

Why has the writer used a dash?

4   "If you don't want me to stay – I won't," sniffed Georgie.   _____

5   Everything returned to normal – well almost!   _____

6   He couldn't walk any further – the pain was too bad.   _____

7   five o'clock – meet Nikki   _____

Cross out the words that are wrong. Write them in correct Standard English.

8   I done the shopping while you was asleep.   _____

9   If they was hungry they could help theirselves to the sandwiches.   _____

10   I could have give you me spare trainers.   _____

X There is only one correct answer.   X There is more than one correct answer.   **23**

Section 2 Test 7

A WARM-UP

Write two adverbs that give different effects.

1 He spoke _____ / _____ .

2 She reacted _____ / _____ .

3 _____ / _____ , he gathered the papers together.

4 The same five-letter string is missing from all these words. Write it in.

d_____ e r   t_____   c _____

Add a three-letter word to complete the longer word.

5 c r _____ u r e

6 g r _____ f u l

7 s t _____ g e

Add a four-, five- or six-letter word to make a longer word.

8 i n _____ a b l e

9 r e _____ m e n t

10 e n _____ e d

B WORD WORK

Add the correct 'shun' ending.

1 discuss_____   confuse_____

2 reduce_____   collide_____

Write the root word and another word with the same root.

	Root word	Words with the same root
3	_____	moisture _____
4	_____	dramatic _____

Write sentences showing the two different meanings of the word.

5 **fan:** _____

6 **fan:** _____

7 **current:** _____

8 **current:** _____

9 **overall:** _____

10 **overall:** _____

C SENTENCE WORK

Expand the notes into a complete sentence.

1 **no sun = no life on Earth** _____

2 **hibernate – survive winter** _____

3 **clouds = water drops** _____

Add words that give the two characters opposing characteristics.
Write the name of the story type.

legend fable folk tale

4 The ladybird _____ and _____ . The grasshopper _____ in the sun. _____

5 Jon was _____ and _____ . His wife was _____ and _____ . _____

6 The Red Knight _____ through the _____ . The Green Knight _____ nearby. _____

Underline the information that is **not** essential to the sentence. Add commas to separate it.

7 Neptune one of the gas giants is the eighth planet from the Sun.

8 Many stringed instruments such as the violin are played with a bow.

9 Hares like rabbits have long ears and powerful hind legs.

10 The iguanadon which was a herbivore was 10 metres long.

X There is only one correct answer.   X There is more than one correct answer.

A WARM-UP

Name the technique used here by the headline writer.

1 **Eggcellent news for Humpty!**

_____

2 **Wanda's wonderful woolly!**

_____

3 **'I was framed' says art thief**

_____

4 Write a headline about Bo Peep.

_____

Add one letter to make the homophone.

5 **not** _____

6 **hole** _____

Add different endings to complete the three words.

7 child_____   child_____   child_____

8 pain_____   pain_____   pain_____

Write the noun as a plural.

9 one wolf → two _____

10 one goose → two _____

B WORD WORK

Add **s** or **c** to complete the words.

1 de__ide   in__ident   in__tant   de__ent

2 __ircuit   __ertain   __alute   __ement

3 ra__e   fan__y   promi__e   i__e

Make opposites by adding the same prefix to all three words.

4 ____mist   ____compose   ____frost

5 ____mount   ____connect   ____mantle

6 ____-starter   ____-drip   ____-smoker

7 ____equal   ____healthy   ____certain

Write three onomatopoeic words to suit each setting.

8 **building site** _____

9 **deserted house** _____

10 **riverbank** _____

C SENTENCE WORK

Continue the sentence in the style of a traditional story.

1 And so a great banquet was held _____

2 But on the third night _____

3 There was once a tiger _____

What sort of answer does each question need: explanation, opinion, fact or description?

4 When was the King born? _____

5 What did the thief look like? _____

6 Why are rain clouds grey? _____

7 What did you think of the film? _____

Underline the correct word of the two that appear in brackets.

8 Do you know (whose / who's) coming?

9 Do you know (whose / who's) book this is?

10 We (were / we're) on time, but now (were / we're) late.

X There is only one correct answer.   X There is more than one correct answer.

25

Section 2 Test 9

A WARM-UP

Rewrite each sentence to say **when**, **where** and **what for**.

1 He begged. _____

_____

_____

2 He travelled. _____

_____

_____

Join the prefix to its meaning.

3 **auto**   distant

4 **bi**   round

5 **circum**   self

6 **tele**   two

7 Write six words that start with **hand**.

_____

_____

Add the missing vowels.

8 m _ n _ t _ s   **10** J _ n _ _ r y

9 f _ m _ l y

B WORD WORK

1 Underline the words that begin with a soft **g**.

gentle gallop gym geography golf

2 Write three more words beginning with a soft **g**.

_____

3 Add the missing **c** or **s**.

o _ e a n   a n _ i e n t   v e r _ e

Underline the correct spelling.

4 dredfully dreadfully dreadfuly

5 furyous furrious furious

6 hurridly hurriedly huriedly

Write two antonyms for each word.

7 love _____

8 good _____

9 soft _____

10 Underline the word that has no opposite.

happy red bright little

C SENTENCE WORK

Continue the sentence to explain why.

1 Every year thousands of trees are cut down _____

2 Water is essential to life on Earth _____

3 Yeast is often added to bread _____

4 Myths are called traditional stories _____

Rewrite the sentence, replacing the common noun in **bold** with a more descriptive noun phrase.

5 He saw **a man**. _____

6 **A woman** stood nearby. _____

7 He saw **a man**. _____

8 **A woman** stood nearby. _____

Add commas, full stops and capital letters to make these texts make sense.

9 Holding onto the side he kicked his legs the boat moved

10 Tess smiled her mother Lucy laughed out loud

X There is only one correct answer.   X There is more than one correct answer.

Section 2   Test 10

A   WARM-UP

Emily admits she was wrong.

Rewrite the sentence as

1 **past tense:**

_____

2 **future tense:**

_____

3 **direct speech:**

_____

4 **an order:**

_____

5 **a question:**

_____

6 Write the verbs in the past tense.

envy _____

spray _____

occupy _____

Add the missing syllable or syllables.

7 i m _____ t a n t   *Clue: vital*

8 d i s _____ t i n g   *Clue: horrible*

9 a _____ i s h _____   *Clue: surprise*

10 p r e _____ t i o n   *Clue: forecast*

B   WORD WORK

1 Add the missing letter.

t e m p t _ t i o n   e m _ t i o n

p o l l _ t i o n   c o m p l _ t i o n

p o s _ t i o n

2 Add the same ending to all three words.

Clue: occupations

opti_____   electri_____   mathemati_____

Write two more occupations with the same ending.

3 _____   4 _____

Write a definition.

5 **transform:** _____

6 **translate:** _____

7 **transport:** _____

8 Write four more words with the root **trans**.

_____

Add the root that will complete all three words.

9 _____national   _____act   _____net

10 _____nology   _____nical   _____nique

C   SENTENCE WORK

Rewrite the sentence, changing the word order as you do so.

1 The Duchess looked down sadly on the little town from up in her tower.

_____

2 The film star came through the door accompanied by two men.

_____

3 He ran to the door immediately on hearing the footsteps.

_____

Use onomatopoeic words to complete the sentence.

4 The machine began to _____ and _____ .

5 The geese _____ , the cows _____ and the horses _____ . What a noise!

6 Alone in the forest, I listened to the _____ of the wind and the _____ of the branches.

7 The city _____ with the _____ of traffic and the _____ of people.

Continue the sentence after the punctuation mark.

8 Many objects are made from wood: _____

9 The rock is porous (_____

10 The door slammed – _____

Section 2 Test 11

A WARM-UP

1 Continue the sentence so that it is at least 25 words long.

Suddenly he stopped _____

_____

_____

_____

Write the antonym.

2 **forward** _____

3 **increase** _____

4 **fearful** _____

5 Write four words that start with **light**.

_____

6 Write four words that end with **light**.

_____

Add the missing letters.
Clue: use the name of a different part of the body to complete each word

7 c h _____ i n g   **9** s _____ c h

8 s u r _____   **10** w _____

B WORD WORK

Underline the correct spelling.

1 germ jerm gurm

2 justise justice gustice

3 gorjous gorgous gorgeous

Write a definition of the word in **bold**, found on a food safety poster.

4 **hygienic:** _____

5 **disposable:** _____

6 **contaminated:** _____

In your own words, rewrite the phrase in **bold**.

7 If you **put your foot in it**

you _____

8 If you **put your feet up**

you _____

9 If you **put your foot down**

you _____

10 If you **have your feet on the ground**

you _____

C SENTENCE WORK

Combine the three sentences into one.

1 The man had magic shoes. The man wore the shoes every day. The shoes wore out.

_____

2 Ursula sold all her hats. She kept one hat. This one hat was Ursula's favourite.

_____

3 Out came an old man. The old man walked down the path. The path led to the village.

_____

Add appropriate nouns and adjectives.

4 Some jellyfish have _____ that can give a _____ .

5 Crocodiles are _____ found in _____ .

6 Mercury is a _____ covered with _____ .

7 A frog's skin is _____ , while a toad's is _____ .

Underline the correct word of the three that appear in brackets.

8 There are two doctors. This is the (doctors / doctor's / doctors') surgery.

9 That is the home (teams / team's / teams') dressing room.

10 That is the (childrens / children's / childrens') playground.

X There is only one correct answer.   X There is more than one correct answer.

Section 2 Test 12

A WARM-UP

Complete the sentence.

1 Only as the clock _____

_____

2 Then, from far and near, _____

_____

3 By recycling, _____

_____

4 Write the verbs in the past tense.

flop _____ **cram** _____

plead _____ **shrug** _____

Write three words that start with

5 over: _____

6 out: _____

Add the missing syllable.
Clue: types of writing

7 e x _____ n a t i o n **9** i n _____ t i o n s

8 p e r _____ s i v e **10** n a r _____ t i v e

B WORD WORK

Add a word before or after the hyphen.

1 e-_____   x-_____

2 free-_____   free-_____

3 _____-energy   _____-friendly

4 _____-free   _____-free

Cross out the words that are
wrong. Write the correct spellings.

5 The caive was cramed with emralds.

_____

6 A terrable monster garded the enterance.

_____

Write a definition of the word in **bold**, found in
an art gallery.

7 **landscape:** _____

8 **portrait:** _____

Write a definition of the word in **bold**, found in a
word-processing program.

9 **landscape:** _____

10 **portrait:** _____

C SENTENCE WORK

Add a phrase or clause that gives extra information.

1 The man, _____, climbed out of the window.

2 And so, _____, the land of Safara was free once more.

3 Vitamin C, _____, helps to repair wounds.

4 Queen Victoria, _____, reigned for 63 years.

She peeked inside. And what do you think she saw?

5 Why does the story writer use this question? _____

Write three similar questions.

6 _____ **7** _____

8 _____

Reporter: Amy, is it true that you are going to live in America?

Amy Starlet: No comment.

9 Write the complete text as reported speech.

_____

_____

10 Write the reporter's question as direct speech in a story.

_____

_____

Section 2 Writing task: The tortoise and the hare

Task

You probably know the story of the tortoise and the hare. In this story, a slow but steady tortoise beats the fast but over-confident hare. Write your own version of this story to appeal to readers aged between eight and 10 years.

Hints

Before you start:

- Picture the scene as the animals prepare for the race. Imagine it using all your senses.
- Make a note of the main events that you want to cover.
- Decide how you will create a vivid picture for your readers.
- Plan how you will make the characters and events appealing.

As you write:

- Think about your audience and how to tell the story effectively.
- Think carefully as you choose your words and storytelling techniques.
- Try out sentences in your head to see how they sound. Then write them down.

Continue on a separate sheet.

Check

- When you have finished, check through your story.
- Edit and proofread it.
- Make sure that everything looks and sounds right.

Section 2 Proofreading task: Fruity fruit salad

Task
Proofread this recipe.

Hints
- Check that everything is clear and sounds right.
- Check that the punctuation and capital letters are correct.
- Check the spelling.

You culd make this colorfull fruit salad for a speshal famly occation its realy delishous.

1 Peel core and chop the appels into wedjes and imediutely toss them in lemen joose. (Worning be carefull when using nifes allways ask an adult to help.

2 Deeseed the grape's half the strawberrys and brake sevral satsumes into segmunts.

3 Plaice all the fruit in a larje bowl togever with eny joose you has colectid. during the preperashun.

4 Carefuly meshure out 100ml of orinje joose and poor over the fruit to moisun it stir gentley with a woodern spoon.

5 Slise too kiwi fruit and kept these for decarashun.

6 Left for about 20 minites just long enuffh to let the flavor's cumbine. Once ready serve to you're gests and let evryone injoy itt

Extra
On a separate sheet of paper, write out either a simple recipe of your own, or instructions for making a birthday card.

Section 3 Test 1

A WARM-UP

Write four sentences using these words only.

into swiftly the rode he night

1 _____

2 _____

3 _____

4 _____

Add one letter to make a new word.

5 **plant**   _____

6 **chef**   _____

7 **cover**   _____

Add the same suffix to complete all three words.

8 poison_____   prosper_____   hazard_____

9 miser_____   respect_____   suit_____

10 tropic_____   post_____   nature_____

B WORD WORK

Complete the word sum.

1 **shovel + ing** = _____

2 **red   + ish** = _____

3 **fit   + est** = _____

4 What spelling rule did you use?

_____

_____

Add the correct prefix.

in im il ir

5 ____possible   ____legal

6 ____responsible   ____accurate

7 All these prefixes mean _____ .

What does the adjective tell you?

8 an **aquatic** animal

The animal _____

9 a **futuristic** car

The car _____

10 stores **nationwide**

The stores _____

C SENTENCE WORK

Rewrite the three sentences as one. Do this in three different ways.

It was snowing. Mick stayed at home. He stayed snug by the fire.

1 _____

2 _____

3 _____

Rewrite the sentence so that it sounds as it would in a report.

4 The monkey kept leaping around. _____

5 Some things stick to the magnet and some jump away.

_____

6 The floppy-eared elephant swings his trunk sadly.

_____

Add commas, full stops and capital letters to make the meaning clear.

7 Little Jimmy was fed up too he sat on the floor refusing to move

8 In less than a minute the entire village vanished yes vanished into thin air

9 As the Prince rode he sang to raise his spirits of course he hoped no-one would hear

10 Amazed at his good fortune Jas won tickets for the Final he was so lucky!

X There is only one correct answer.   X There is more than one correct answer.

Section 3 Test 2

A WARM-UP

Complete the sentence to give a different view
of the character.

1 "I know," _____ Abby, _____
_____

2 "I know," _____ Abby, _____
_____

3 "I know," _____ Abby, _____

Read the title and guess the type of story.

4 **The Enchanted Piper**   _____

5 **Tiddles – the Supercat!**   _____

6 **The Curse of Bleak Towers**   _____

7 Make three words.

   tele photo ic graph

   _____

Draw a line to join the root to its meaning.

8 **tele**   to write

9 **graph**   light

10 **photo**   distant

B WORD WORK

Add the same two letters to complete both words.

1 f a c t __ __ y   c a t e g __ __ y

2 i n t __ __ e s t   l i t __ __ a c y

Add a suffix to the word in **bold**.
Use the new word to complete the sentence.

3 He was a **king** without a _____ .

4 We all need the _____ of a **friend**.

5 She paid her _____ fee and

   became a **member** of the club.

6 The **hero** behaved _____ .

Use a root word and the suffix **tion**
to complete the sentence.

pollute irrigate purify consume

7 Factory waste can cause water _____ .

8 _____ makes water safe to drink.

9 _____ is vital for crops to grow.

10 Find ways to cut water _____ .

C SENTENCE WORK

We can all help to save the planet, starting right now.

Rewrite the sentence as

1 **an imperative:** _____

2 **an exclamation:** _____

3 **a rhetorical question:** _____

Write **definite** or **possibility** beside each statement.

4 I will do that tomorrow.   _____

5 I might do that tomorrow.   _____

6 Maybe I'll do that tomorrow.   _____

7 I could do that tomorrow.   _____

Add an extra piece of information about the character, with a comma before and after.

8 Simeon _____ was waiting.

9 Mr Sprott _____ glared at the young urchin.

10 Marianne _____ liked living in the old house.

X There is only one correct answer.   X There is more than one correct answer.

Section 3 Test 3

A WARM-UP

Complete the sentence in different ways.

1 He hurried on as if _____

_____

2 He hurried on in case _____

_____

Add the same four-letter word to complete all the longer words.

3 i n t e _____

4 _____ a u r a n t

5 a r _____ e d

Use a pair of homophones to complete the sentence.

6 After a w_____ , he was too w_____ to move.

7 The lady m_____ her m_____ carry the bags.

Add the same suffix to all three words.

8 awe_____   fear_____   hand_____

9 like_____   length_____   clock_____

10 back_____   home_____   on _____

B WORD WORK

Write the word split into syllables.
Draw a ring round the vowel that is difficult to hear and makes the word tricky to spell.

1 different   _____ / _____ / _____

2 desperate   _____ / _____ / _____

3 definite   _____ / _____ / _____

Write the verb that comes from the noun.

4 knee   → to _____

5 television → to _____

6 class   → to _____

7 wide   → to _____

8 editor   → to _____

Write two definitions.

9 **shed:** _____

10 **shed:** _____

C SENTENCE WORK

Which story is for 4–6 year olds and which is for 7–10 year olds?

1 So Jack swapped Daisy the cow for a little bag of magic beans.   _____

2 So Jack (the twit) gave away the cow for a pile of (supposedly) magic beans.   _____

Give a reason for your answer.

3 The first story _____

4 The second story _____

Write three words that would sound correct if used to fill the gap.

5 He walked _____ the wall.   _____

6 The book was _____ the desk.   _____

7 We had pizza _____ the film.   _____

8 Underline the word type that identifies the words you have chosen.

nouns pronouns prepositions

Add the apostrophes to this magic spell.

9 Mix the spots from four leopards coats with two wasps stings and a peacocks feather.

10 Sprinkle with the dust from six butterflies wings and the shine from a unicorns horn.

Section 3 Test 4

A WARM-UP

Add a phrase or a clause to the start of the sentence.

1 _____ the men

were hungry.

2 _____ the men

were hungry.

Write four onomatopoeic words.

3 cl_____   cl_____   cl_____   cl_____

4 sl_____   sl_____   sl_____   sl_____

5 cr_____   cr_____   cr_____   cr_____

Add the correct 'shun' ending and write the word.

6 **music**   _____

7 **collide**   _____

8 **create**   _____

9 **possess**   _____

10 **imagine**   _____

B WORD WORK

1 Underline the long vowel sound.

   pie veil view shield

   pier rein fiery their

2 What do you notice?

_____

_____

Sort the words into four groups.

3 **ee sound:**   _____

4 **i sound:**   _____

5 **long a sound:**   _____

6 **other sounds:**   _____

7 How are the long **a** sounds spelt?

_____

8 Write four words using the root word **act**.

_____

Write a definition of the word **conductor**, as found in

9 **a music book:**   _____

10 **a science book:**   _____

_____

C SENTENCE WORK

Rewrite the sentence so that it gives the same information, but as a **possibility**, not a definite fact.

1 It will be a better day tomorrow.   _____

2 In the future we will drive electric cars.   _____

Rewrite the sentence so that it gives the same information, but sounds more **definite**, rather than a possibility.

3 Your money could make a difference.   _____

4 Your efforts might help save the planet.   _____

Add powerful verbs to describe the actions of

5 **a hero:** He _____ his sword, _____ onto the white stallion and _____ away.

6 **a wild animal:** It _____ up and _____ , _____ at the air.

7 **a fire:** It _____ through the wood, _____ the trees and _____ ever closer.

Add the punctuation to these headlines.

8 Merlins the name magics his game

9 Is the polar bears Arctic world about to melt

10 Pupils art on display

A WARM-UP

Write three sentences (S), a question (Q) and an imperative (I) using these words only.

you do better should really

1 S: _____

2 S: _____

3 S: _____

4 Q: _____

5 I: _____

Read aloud the list of words. Listen to their sounds. Underline the odd one out.

6 pour your flour tour

7 daughter laughter slaughter

8 rein veil either weigh

Underline two antonyms of the word in **bold**.

9 **slow** rapid laze brisk dawdle

10 **light** dim weighty joyful pale

B WORD WORK

Use a different three-letter word to complete each longer word.

Clue: each word starts with p

1 c o m ____ y

2 h o s ____ a l

3 How does breaking words down like this help you to spell them?

_____

_____

These prefixes mean **not**.
Write two words that begin with each one.

4 **ir** _____

5 **il** _____

6 **ir** is added if _____

7 **il** is added if _____

Give a definition of the word in **bold**, found in notes for a design and technology project.

8 **reinforced** frame: _____

9 **mouldable** materials: _____

10 **compressed** material: _____

C SENTENCE WORK

Complete the sentence.

1 Along the riverbank, _____

2 During the night, _____

3 At the station, _____

Write the text type that each text is taken from. Give a reason to support your answer.

Press the standby button on the remote control.

4 From: _____ **5** Reason: _____

Clearly, we must stop this from happening!

6 From: _____ **7** Reason: _____

Rome, the capital city of Italy, stands on the banks of the River Tiber.

8 From: _____ **9** Reason: _____

Add two commas and a dash so that this sentence makes sense.

10 When he heard this Joe began to laugh not because it was funny but because he was relieved to find that no-one knew the truth.

X There is only one correct answer.   X There is more than one correct answer.

Section 3   Test 6

A WARM-UP

Complete the sentence in two ways.

1 _____ , she shivered

_____

2 _____ , she shivered

_____

Add the missing syllables.

3 _____ f e n c e _____   *Clue: vulnerable, weak, frail*

4 _____ g u s t _____   *Clue: shocked*

5 m e s _____ _____   *Clue: one who carries a message*

6 _____ d a n _____   *Clue: to risk, threaten*

Complete these words from other languages.

7 s p a g _____   *Clue: food (Italian)*

8 k a r _____   *Clue: entertainment (Japanese)*

9 g u i _____   *Clue: musical instrument (Spanish)*

10 d u n _____   *Clue: clothing (Hindi)*

B WORD WORK

Add two more words with similar spellings.

1 cinema circle   _____

2 cereal celebrity   _____

3 gentle germ   _____

4 cycle Cyprus   _____

5 Add the same prefix to all these words.

*Clue: it means **not***

____possible   ____patient

____mature   ____mobile

6 What do you notice about the root words?

_____

Write the opposite of these maths terms.

7 ascending   _____

8 positive   _____

9 probable   _____

10 maximum   _____

C SENTENCE WORK

Use the connectives to make a case for a Walking Bus scheme.

A Walking Bus scheme has many advantages.

1 For example, _____

2 Indeed, _____

3 In addition, _____

4 Furthermore, _____

Sort these prepositional phrases into different types.

down the street, at midnight, to the cinema, during assembly, at school, between the gates, on Tuesday, after tea, in the shop, on top of the hill, over the fence, towards the hall

5 Showing time: _____

6 Showing position: _____

7 Showing direction: _____

Add the punctuation to this dialogue.

8 Im ungry moaned the monster rubbing his stomach.

9 Youve just had breakfast sighed Jim.

10 Still ungry moaned the monster Very ungry.

X There is only one correct answer.   X There is more than one correct answer.   **37**

Section 3 Test 7

A WARM-UP

Try walking instead of using the car.

Present this idea as

1 **an imperative:** _____

_____

2 **a question:** _____

_____

3 **a slogan:** _____

Split the word to show the prefix, root and suffix.

4 description _____ / _____ / _____

5 unoriginal _____ / _____ / _____

6 informal _____ / _____ / _____

Add a word after the hyphen.

7 hi-_____

8 dog-_____

9 problem-_____

10 in-_____

B WORD WORK

Add **ei** or **ie** to make the long **ee** sound.

1 p___r c e   g r___f

2 c___l i n g   c o n c___t e d

3 What spelling rule did you use?

_____

Add the correct suffix. Make sure the word is spelt correctly.

ism ity

4 hero____   generous____

5 sincere____   tour____

6 Write the words that name special qualities a person might have.

_____

Write **formal** or **informal** beside each word or phrase.

7 **stuck-up**   _____

8 **arrogant**   _____

9 **understand**   _____

10 **get it**   _____

C SENTENCE WORK

This text is from a magazine. Is it written for 4–6 year olds, 7–10 year olds or adults?

1 Get fit for summer, the world's hottest destinations and feel-good food.   _____

2 Full of mind-boggling facts, awesome activities and cool creations.   _____

3 Play new games and join in the fun with Moppy and Sam.   _____

Rewrite the sentence in a way that might appeal to 9–11 year olds.

4 Read about clever new inventions.   _____

5 Learn how you can help save the planet.   _____

6 Find out a lot about bats.   _____

Use a dash to add information to the end of the sentence.

7 Don't throw newspapers away _____

8 Spiders live in many different places _____

Use commas to embed extra information within the sentence.

9 William Shakespeare _____ is well known all over the world.

10 The pyramids _____ are amazing buildings.

38

X There is only one correct answer.   X There is more than one correct answer.

Section 3   Test 8

A   WARM-UP

Complete this sentence using different prepositional phrases.

1   Oliver waited _____

2   Oliver waited _____

3   Oliver waited _____

4   Oliver waited _____

Add a homophone to complete the joke.

5   **Question:** Which vegetable can sink a boat?

   Clue: it's long, green and white

   Answer: A   l _ _ _ !

6   **Waiter:** It's b _ _ _   soup, sir.

7   **Customer:** I don't care what it's b _ _ _
   before, what is it now?

Write the meaning of the letters.

8   CD   _____

9   ROM   _____

10   pc   _____

B   WORD WORK

Add the missing vowels. Draw a ring round the vowel sound that is difficult to hear.

1   e _ s _ l y

2   b _ s _ n e s s

3   d _ _ f _ n i n g

4   w _ d _ n i n g

Add a suffix and write the new word.

ise   ify

5   **magnet**   _____

6   **sign**   _____

7   Underline the word type that best describes the root words above.

   nouns   adjectives   verbs

8   Underline the word type that best describes the new words above.

   nouns   adjectives   verbs

Write the noun that is linked to the adjective.

9   **strong**   _____

10   **clear**   _____

C   SENTENCE WORK

Continue the sentence as

1   **a traditional tale:** She came to _____

2   **a fantasy:** She came to _____

3   **a mystery story:** She came to _____

Rewrite the sentence in a more formal way.

4   I think a new leisure centre would be really cool. _____

   _____

5   There's not much else we can do. _____

6   We asked lots of people and nearly everyone said it would be great. _____

   _____

Put a tick if the apostrophe is used correctly. Put a cross if it is not. Explain your answer.

7   India's monsoon season _____

8   No-ones' sure. _____

9   "Where are you goin' then, laddy?" he asked. _____

10   Six tree's were chopped down. _____

A   WARM-UP

Write three sentences, each one using the word **flat** in a different way.

flat parcel

1 _____

2 _____

3 _____

_____

Use a different four-letter word to complete each longer word.

Clue: each word starts with **t**

4 d e _____ i n e d

5 p r o _____ e d

6 a t _____ i o n

Use the word to make up a pun or a word-play phrase.

7 **peas** _____

8 **tea** _____

9 **cat** _____

10 **snow** _____

B   WORD WORK

Add three different suffixes and write the new words.

1 **strange** _____

2 **tune** _____

3 **use** _____

4 Draw a ring round the vowel suffixes. Then underline the consonant suffixes.

5 What pattern do you notice for adding suffixes to words ending with **e**?

_____

_____

_____

Underline the correct word of the two that appear in brackets.

6 It was a ten (story / storey) building.

7 Blood contains red and white (cells / sells).

8 A (vain / vein) carries blood to the heart.

Add the missing part of the word.

9 advert _____

10 _____ plane

C   SENTENCE WORK

Use the dash to add a comment that makes the sentence sound more informal.

1 Miss Edgar was very angry – _____

2 Mum took Nikki's side – _____

3 It rained every day of our holiday – _____

4 We are going to win the league this year – _____

Sort the connectives into two groups.

on the other hand, certainly, however, clearly, furthermore, in contrast

5 **Making a case in favour:** _____

6 **Giving an opposing view:** _____

7 Write three more connectives that you might use to put the case **for** something.

_____

Add punctuation and capital letters.

8 Dont cried cyril whatever you do dont turn round

9 Mr Jenkins a 26-year-old plumber told our reporter I didn't see the bus until it was too late

10 Jack Spellings book begins with the line Humphrey Norton's life was a mess

X There is only one correct answer.   X There is more than one correct answer.

Section 3　Test 10

A　WARM-UP

1 Write an acrostic poem about rain.

R _____

A _____

I _____

N _____

Add the missing vowel to each syllable.

2 d__ f / f __ r / __ n c e

3 r __ f / __ r / __ n c e

4 c __ n / f __ r / __ n c e

Complete these compound words.

Clue: all computer terms

5 net_____

6 up_____

7 down_____

8 on_____

9 tool_____

10 short_____

B　WORD WORK

1 Underline the odd one out.

yield　brief　weird　thief　piece

2 Why is the odd one out unusual?

_____

_____

Add the same prefix to both words.

3 ____ject　____duce　　**5** ____ceed　____cept

4 ____pect　____pense　　**6** ____close　____joy

Write a definition of the word in **bold**.

7 Select the **channel** you want to view.

channel: _____

8 He was the first to swim the **Channel**.

Channel: _____

_____

9 It was a **joint** attempt.

joint: _____

10 Your wrist **joint** allows you to move your hand.

joint: _____

C　SENTENCE WORK

These lovely creatures have lived here for centuries but sadly they are now endangered.

1 What is the writer's view of this situation? _____

2 What is the writer's view of these creatures? _____

3 Which two words show the writer's opinion? _____

Continue the text with

4 **a follow-up sentence:** _____

5 **a follow-up question:** _____

6 **a follow-up imperative:** _____

7 What is the writer's purpose? Tick two.

to instruct ____　　to persuade ____　　to inform ____　　to entertain ____

Check the use of apostrophes.

8 Balloons' were tied to the two donkey's tail's.

9 Hercules' carried the two sisters shopping all the way to Marys' house.

10 The clocks finger's slowly ticked round as they waited for the chiefs signal.

Section 3 Test 11

A WARM-UP

Write two sentences using these words.

doorway darkness

Use a different connective in each.

1 _____

_____

_____

2 _____

_____

_____

Write the homophone.

3 key _____   **5** him _____

4 waist _____   **6** serial _____

Write two words using the root word.

7 hyper _____

8 inter _____

9 mega _____

10 eco _____

B WORD WORK

1 Add the missing syllable to each word.

int / _____ / est   gen / _____ / al

sep / _____ / ate   av / _____ / age

2 What do you notice about the missing syllables?

_____

3 _____ is the odd one out because

_____

4 Add a suffix to make a verb.

active _____   **mobile** _____

simple _____   **dark** _____

Use one of the verbs in each sentence.

5 The sky began to _____ .

6 "_____ the machine!" said Dr Brains.

7 We need to _____ the wording.

8 The King began to _____ his forces.

Write three words linked in meaning and spelling to the word in **bold**.

9 cycle _____

10 human _____

C SENTENCE WORK

Give two reasons why the writer might have changed this sentence as shown.

We know this is wrong. Every right-thinking person knows this is utterly wrong.

1 _____

2 _____

Rewrite this sentence so that it sounds more persuasive.

3 Every child should have a place to live. _____

Complete the sentence using a simile.

4 He moved like _____   **6** She clucked like _____

5 Kapil followed like _____   **7** Azara behaves like _____

Write this text as direct speech, using a new line for each item.

The man wanted to speak to the Chief. I asked him to leave, but the man said it was urgent.

8 _____

9 _____

10 _____

42

X There is only one correct answer.   X There is more than one correct answer.

A WARM-UP

Fruit is good for you.

Make this idea sound more appealing using

1 alliteration: _____

_____

2 rhyme: _____

_____

3 a pun or word play: _____

_____

Add a three-letter word to complete the longer word.

4 v o l ___ o   6 c o n ___ u e

5 c o m ___ e r   7 i n g ___ i e n t s

Add three of these suffixes to the
root word to make three new words.

er en y ly ness

8 shake _____

9 wide _____

10 glad _____

B WORD WORK

Add the missing letters.

1 v ___ n   *Clue: carries blood round the body*

2 r e c ___ v e   *Clue: to be given something*

3 a n c ___ n t   *Clue: very old*

4 f ___ r c e   *Clue: vicious*

Add the suffix **ity** and write the new word.

5 secure   _____

6 popular   _____

7 human   _____

8 What type of words have you made?

_____

Write two definitions of the word in **bold**.

9 table

in maths: _____

another meaning: _____

10 fast

in religious education (RE): _____

_____

another meaning: _____

C SENTENCE WORK

Oliver sat up suddenly. The room was completely dark. What had woken him?

Write three ways in which the writer builds suspense.

1 _____   3 _____

2 _____

Write the next sentence, further building the suspense.

   4 _____

Rewrite the sentence with the ideas in a different order.

5 We need to raise more money to continue our valuable work.

_____

6 There will be no open spaces left if we continue to build more houses.

_____

7 They waited for his return while the sun began to sink behind the rooftops.

_____

Add commas, full stops and capital letters to make the meaning clear.

8 Overall the film is stunning from opening scene to thrilling ending you will be gripped.

9 He looked everywhere he searched every box every drawer every hiding place.

10 We need to raise money we need your help without it more birds will die.

Now complete Section 3 of the Progress chart on page 46.   **43**

Section 3 Writing task: Outraged

Task

You read in the newspaper that your local library or playing field is to be shut down – choose the one that would mean the most to you. You are outraged by this news. Your task is to write a letter to protest about the closure. Try to persuade everyone that this is wrong.

Hints

Before you start:

- Remind yourself how a letter should be structured.
- Think about the points you will make.
- How will you explain and support these points?
- What methods of persuasion will you use?

As you write:

- Make your arguments sound strong and convincing.
- Choose carefully both your words and your persuasive techniques.
- Try out phrases and sentences to see if they sound convincing.

Continue on a separate sheet.

Check

- When you have finished, check through your letter.
- Edit and proofread it.
- Make sure that everything looks and sounds right.

Section 3 Proofreading task: The genie of the bedside lamp

Task
Proofread this scene from a playscript.

Hints
- Do the sentences sound right?
- Are the punctuation and capital letters correct?
- Do all the spellings look right?

Seen 2 in the bedroom what is a real mess

Emily in astonishment Look at this mess what happaned the carpit's ruind and Dads prize CD collecshun is damiged. whats he going to say

Ben snapilly Hes not going to say nothing becuase itll be tidi before he get back.

Emily in disbelief are you insane thats inposserble your defenetely in truble this time

Ben siying Im probubley going to rigret this but watch
Ben picks up the bedside lamp and gave it a rub, there is a deafning roar Emily let out a shreik as a jenie apears floating by the seiling.

Emily trembeling what is that

Ben impashentely A genie of corse.

Emily But but thats not posserble is it

Extra
On a separate sheet of paper, continue the same playscript or write brief notes on what happens next.

English Skills 4 Progress chart

Name		Class/Set	
Teacher's name		Date	

Instructions

Read the **'I can' targets** for the section you have just finished.

- Colour the circle **green** if you find it **easy** to do what is described.
- Colour the circle **orange** if you are **getting there**, but still need to work on it.
- Colour the circle **red** if you still find this a **difficult** thing to do.

If there are things that you still find difficult you can work on them in the next section or in the next book.

Writing sentences

'I can' targets	Section 1	Section 2	Section 3
I can write simple, compound and complex sentences.	○	○	○
I can reorder and vary sentences for effect and to suit different text types.	○	○	○
I can vary my choice of conjunctions (e.g., **as if**, **though** …) to join sentences.		○	○
I can form noun phrases using adjectives, prepositions and words like **which** or **who**.			○

Using punctuation

	Section 1	Section 2	Section 3
I can punctuate the start and end of sentences, avoiding comma splice.	○	○	○
I can use commas to separate words, phrases and clauses.	○	○	○
I can use speech marks, new lines and correct punctuation in direct speech.	○	○	○
I can use the apostrophe for possession and in shortened forms.	○	○	○
I can write sentences using dashes, brackets and colons.	○	○	○
I can proofread my writing and use punctuation to make the meaning clear.		○	○

Checking grammar

	Section 1	Section 2	Section 3
I can use the language features of different texts (e.g., instructions).	○	○	○
I can select the right tense to use in different types of writing.	○	○	○
I can use direct and reported speech.	○	○	○
I can use modal verbs to show shades of meaning.	○	○	○
I can use Standard English in my writing.		○	○

Understanding and choosing words

	Section 1	Section 2	Section 3
I can choose words for effect (e.g., to suggest mood or for emphasis).	○	○	○
I can choose words to match the type of text (e.g., formal or informal).	○	○	○
I can choose words very carefully, thinking about shades of meaning.	○	○	○
I can use similes and metaphors in my descriptions.	○	○	○
I can use word structure and origin to help me work out word meanings.	○	○	○
I can explain the meaning of common idioms and everyday metaphors.	○	○	○
I can explain the difference between everyday and specialist word meanings.			○

Spelling

	Section 1	Section 2	Section 3
I can use word structure (e.g., roots, prefixes, suffixes) to help me with spelling.	○	○	○
I can use spelling rules to add prefixes and suffixes to roots.	○	○	○
I can choose the correct spelling of homophones (e.g., **rain/reign**).	○	○	○
I can look for familiar patterns to help me with spelling (e.g., **ie/ei**, soft **c**).	○	○	○
I can spell words with unstressed vowels (e.g., **different**, **general**, **factory**).		○	○
I can choose the correct spelling of similar suffixes (e.g., **tion/sion**, **ible/able**).		○	○

Published by Schofield & Sims Ltd,
Dogley Mill, Fenay Bridge, Huddersfield HD8 0NQ, UK
Telephone 01484 607080

www.schofieldandsims.co.uk

Copyright © Schofield and Sims Ltd, 2011
Fourth impression 2012

Author: Carol Matchett
Carol Matchett has asserted her moral right under the Copyright, Designs and Patents Act, 1988, to be identified as the author of this work.

British Library Cataloguing in Publication Data
A catalogue record for this book is available from the British Library.

Commissioning and editorial project management by
Carolyn Richardson Publishing Services (www.publiserve.co.uk)

Design by **Ledgard Jepson Ltd**
Printed in the UK by **Wyndeham Gait Ltd**, Grimsby, Lincolnshire

English Skills 4 ISBN 978 07217 1178 2; Essential English Skills 4 ISBN 978 07217 1191 1

Schofield&Sims

the long-established educational publisher specialising in maths, literacy and science

English Skills provides graded questions that develop pupils' literacy skills at Key Stage 2. Key areas are constantly revisited, giving pupils the intensive practice that is essential if they are to become fully literate.

Every **English Skills** book is divided into three sections, each comprising 12 one-page tests. Some questions have more than one correct answer, and these are indicated using a simple key.

Every test page provides:
- Part A: 10 **Warm-up** questions – puzzles and other activities that focus on areas covered earlier
- Part B: 10 **Word work** questions – covering **spelling**, **word structure** and **vocabulary**
- Part C: 10 **Sentence work** questions – covering **sentence formation**, **punctuation** and **grammar**.

> **Pupils may answer the test questions independently or in pairs. Before they begin, check that they know how to handle the different question types.**

Each section also contains a **Writing task** and a **Proofreading task**, providing tailor-made contexts in which pupils may apply their developing skills. A **Glossary** defines literacy terms and a **Progress chart** helps them to monitor their own work.

English Skills 4

English Skills 4 is for pupils who can write compound and some complex sentences using conjunctions, phrases, adverbials and varied sentence starters. Able to spell correctly most medium-frequency words, they can identify root words to help them spell and understand unfamiliar words. Designed for Year 5, this book may also be used with older or younger pupils.

It helps pupils learn to:
- experiment with sentence construction
- adapt sentences to suit different purposes
- use commas to separate phrases
- set out and punctuate direct speech
- correct errors in the use of apostrophes

- use brackets, colons and dashes
- spell common words with unstressed vowels
- recognise **im, ir, tion, sion, cian, ible, able**
- use the rules for adding suffixes
- apply knowledge of word origin and roots.

The separate **English Skills 4 Answers** (ISBN 978 07217 1184 3) summarises the key **Focus** of each set of questions and gives answers to facilitate marking. The **Teacher's Guide** (ISBN 978 07217 1187 4) contains an **Entry test**, a **Group record sheet** and other valuable resources, helping you to use the series to its full potential.

The complete range of workbooks is as follows. A separate book of answers is available for each one.

English Skills 1 (for Key Stages 1 & 2)	978 07217 1175 1	**English Skills 4**	978 07217 1178 2
English Skills 2	978 07217 1176 8	**English Skills 5**	978 07217 1179 9
English Skills 3	978 07217 1177 5	**English Skills 6** (for Key Stages 2 & 3)	978 07217 1180 5

ISBN 978-07217-1178-2

FSC MIX Paper from responsible sources www.fsc.org FSC® C022534

ISBN 978 07217 1178 2
Key Stage 2
Age range 7–11 years
£2.95
(Retail price)

For further information and to place your order visit
www.schofieldandsims.co.uk or telephone 01484 607080